101

WONDERS
OF THE
WORLD

Reprinted in 2014 by

An imprint of Om Books International

Corporate & Editorial Office
A 12, Sector 64, Noida 201 301
Uttar Pradesh, India
Phone: +91 120 477 4100
Email:editorial@ombooks.com
Website: www.ombooksinternational.com

Sales Office
4379/4B, Prakash House, Ansari Road
Darya Ganj, New Delhi 110 002, India
Phone: +91 11 2326 3363, 2326 5303
Fax: +91 11 2327 8091
Email: sales@ombooks.com
Website: www.ombooks.com

ISBN: 978-93-80070-78-0

Printed at EIH Press, Gurgaon, India

10 9 8 7 6 5 4 3 2

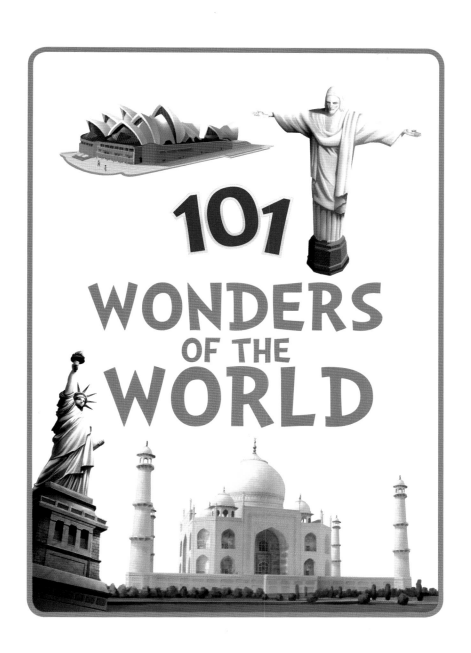

101
WONDERS
OF THE
WORLD

An imprint of Om Books International

Contents

1 Golden Gate Bridge

The Golden Gate Bridge is in San Francisco, U.S. It was designed by engineer Joseph Strauss. The Golden Gate Bridge had the longest span in the world from its completion in 1937 until the Verrazano Narrows Bridge was built in New York in 1964. The main span 4200 feet (1280 m) long, is suspended from two cables hung from towers 746 feet (227 m) high; at midpoint the roadway is 265 feet (81 m) above mean high water. The Golden Gate Bridge is at its most enchanting in the morning when the bridge is often covered in mist. But the bridge is also alluring at night when the lighting makes it seem as if the spires of the towers dissolve in the darkness.

2 Abu Simbel

Abu Simbel is also known as Abu Sunbul. It is in southern Egypt along the River Nile about 290 kilometres southwest of Aswan. It is a site of two temples built by Egyptian King Ramses II. The temples were carved out of a sandstone cliff on the west bank of the River Nile. The temples were shifted to higher ground in the 1960s as the waters of Lake Nasser began to rise following completion of the Aswan High Dam. This was considered a great engineering feat. A very good Sound and Light show has been introduced at Abu Simbel in the evening. This includes projections onto the two temples showing how they once would have looked. It is part of the UNESCO World Heritage Site of 'Nubian Monuments'.

3 Easter Island

Easter Island is one of the most isolated islands in the world. It is situated in the South Pacific Ocean, about 2,350 miles west of Chile. The island was called Rapa Nui by the inhabitants. The name 'Easter Island' was given by a Dutch explorer who discovered it on Easter Sunday in 1722. There are more than 600 huge statues called 'moai' spread over the island, each carved from a single block of soft stone by the Rapa Nui people. Some are more than 30 feet (9 m) high. The island was made into a national park in 1935. It is listed as a UNESCO World Heritage Site.

4 Taj Mahal

This brilliant piece of Mughal architecture is situated in Agra, India, on the southern bank of the River Yamuna. The Taj Mahal was designated a UNESCO World Heritage site in 1983. It is also one of the new Seven Wonders of the World. The Taj Mahal is a mausoleum (burial place).

It was built by the Mughal emperor Shah Jahan (1628–1658) in the memory of his beloved wife, Mumtaz Mahal.

The construction of the Taj Mahal took 22 years, from 1632 to 1654. More than 20,000 workers were employed. The material was brought in from all over India and Central Asia and it took a fleet of 1,000 elephants to transport it to the site. About ₹ 32 crore were spent during the construction of the monument.

The Taj Mahal stands on a square marble base 312 feet on each side and 23 feet high. The building is a square of 186 feet on each side. Atop the entire building is a large onion-shaped dome. It is supported on a tall drum, and the top stands 243 feet above garden level. There are parapets over each arch. Much of the decoration, apart from geometrical designs, consists of verses from the Koran written on the marble. The Taj sparkles in the moonlight when the semiprecious stones in the white marble on the main mausoleum catch the glow of the moon. It is said that the Taj is pinkish in the morning, milky white in the evening and golden when the moon shines.

5 Dead Sea

The Dead Sea lies between Israel and Jordan. Its basin lies some 1,300 feet (400 m) below sea level, making it the lowest body of water in the world. The lake is about 50 miles (80 km) long and 11 miles (18 km) wide. Its surface area is about 394 square miles (1,020 sq km). The Dead Sea is the world's saltiest natural lake. Its near-surface waters are more than eight times as saline as the ocean and the lake's salt concentration increases with depth. The extreme salinity allows humans to float easily, but it prevents all living things except bacteria from inhabiting the lake.

It is known in the Bible as the 'Salt Sea' or the 'Sea of the Arabah'. It is named so because its high mineral content allows nothing to live in its waters. Other post-Biblical names for the Dead Sea include the 'Sea of Sodom,' the 'Sea of Lot,' the 'Sea of Asphalt' and the 'Stinking Sea.'

The Dead Sea is rich in minerals including salt, potash, bromides and bitumen, or native asphalt.

Temperatures at the Dead Sea are very hot in summer and mild in winter.

6 Big Ben

Big Ben is one of London's best-known landmarks. It looks most spectacular at night when the clock faces are illuminated.

The four dials of the clock are 23 square feet, the minute hand is 14 feet long and the figures are 2 feet high.

The name Big Ben actually refers not to the clock tower itself, but to the thirteen ton bell hung within. The bell was named after the first commissioner of works, Sir Benjamin Hall.

The clock tower was completed in 1859 and the Great Clock started on May 31, with the Great Bell first struck time on July 11 and the quarter bells first chimed on September 7.

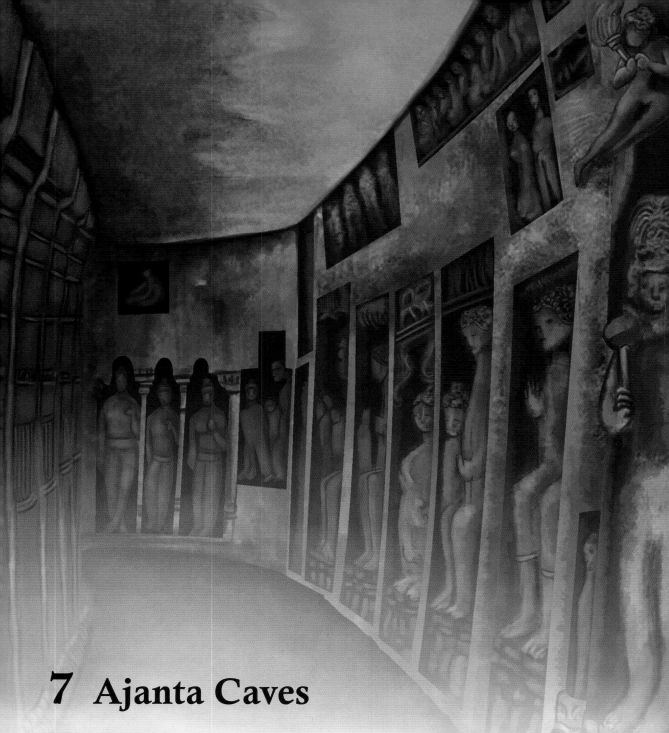

7 Ajanta Caves

The Ajanta Caves are near the Ajanta village, Maharashtra, India. The first Buddhist cave monuments at Ajanta date from the 2nd and 1st centuries bc. There are approximately 30 caves at the site of Ajanta, of which cave numbers 9, 10, 19, 26 and 29 are *caityas* (sanctuaries) and the rest are *vihāras* (monasteries). The carvings and the paintings in the caves depict the life of Lord Buddha. Along with this, several types of human and animal figures are also carved out of the rocks. The caves have been designated as a UNESCO World Heritage Site.

8 Terracotta Warriors

The Terracotta Warriors is part of an elaborate mausoleum created to accompany the first emperor of China into the afterlife, according to archaeologists.

The Terracotta Warriors and horses were discovered accidentally when some local farmers sank a well at the foot of Mt. Lishan in 1974. Excavation was later carried on the site. They found not one, but thousands of clay soldiers, each with unique facial expressions and positioned according to their ranks. Further excavations revealed swords, arrow tips, and other weapons, many in perfect conditions.

The Terracotta Warriors are the most significant archeological discovery of the 20th century in China. They are acclaimed to be on the same level of historical importance as the pyramids of Egypt and the sculptures of ancient Greece. The museum is a major world tourist destination.

9 CN Tower

The Canadian National Tower, better known as CN Tower, is the world's tallest free-standing structure. It is located in Toronto, Canada. The tower was constructed by the Canadian National Railroad to improve television reception. The CN Tower attracts approximately 2 million visitors each year. Though the tower primarily functions for radio and television signals, it also has attractive features for visitors. At the top of the tower are a revolving CN Tower restaurant and lookout platforms.

10 Sahara Desert

The Sahara Desert, which covers most of North Africa, is the largest desert in the world. It covers an area of approximately 3.5 million square miles. On the west, the Sahara is surrounded by the Atlantic Ocean and on the east by the Red Sea, and to the north are the Atlas Mountains and the Mediterranean Sea. The name 'Sahara' comes from the Arabic noun 'sahra', meaning desert, and its plural, 'sahara'.

The sand dunes of the dessert are very big, so huge that they can go up to a height of 600 feet. Additionally, there are stone plateaus, salt flats, gravel plains and arid valleys. Sandstorms are very common in the desert.

The highest part of the desert is at the summit of Mount Koussi, which is 11,204 feet (3,415 m) high. The lowest point of the Sahara is 436 feet (133 m) below sea level in the Qattera Depression in Egypt.

The plant life is thin with scattered concentrations of grasses and shrubs. There are many animals in the desert, including poisonous snakes and poisonous spiders, scorpions, monitor lizards, sand vipers, wild dogs, ostriches, cheetahs, among others.

11 Shwedagon Pagoda

The Shwedagon Pagoda is in Myanmar. It is also known as the Shwedagon Paya. The Pagoda is 321.5 feet high. Its top is made up of gold and has lots of diamonds, rubies and precious gems set in it. It is a stunning work of Burmese temple architecture and is the holiest Buddhist shrine in Myanmar.

The legend of the Schwedagon Pagoda begins with two Burmese merchant brothers who met the Buddha himself. The Buddha gave them eight of his hairs to be enshrined in Burma. With the help of spirits and the king of the region, the brothers discovered the hill where the relics of the previous Buddhas had been enshrined. This is where the pagoda was built.

12 Varanasi

Varanasi, also known as Benares, Banaras, Kashi or Kasi, is on the banks of the Ganges River in Uttar Pradesh. It is the world's oldest living city. The city is considered the most sacred place for all Hindus.

The name 'Varanasi' is derived from the twin tributaries of Ganga, Varuna and Asi. Varanasi is chiefly known to travellers for its ghats (stone steps leading directly into the water).

The city is also a centre of arts and crafts and of music and dance. Varanasi is famous for silk weaving and its silk saris with gold and silver threadwork, as well as for wooden toys, bangles made of glass, ivory work and its brassware.

13 Mount Everest

The Everest lies in the Himalayan mountain range along the border of Nepal and Tibet. It is the highest mountain in the world at a height of 29,035 feet (8850 m). Its Tibetan name is *Chomolungma* meaning 'Goddess Mother of the World' or 'Goddess of the Valley.' In Sanskrit it is known as *Sagarmatha* meaning 'Ocean Mother.' Mount Everest is named after Sir George Everest, who was the British Surveyor-General of India from 1830 to 1843. Sir Edmund Hillary and Sherpa Tenzing Norgay became the first men known to have reached the Everests' summit in 1953.

The Everest has a temperature of about -33° Fahrenheit (-36° Celcius) and can drop as low as -76° Fahrenheit (-60° Celcius). Many men and women have risked their lives to climb the mountain.

14 Iguazu Falls

Iguaza Falls are a series of waterfalls at the Argentina-Brazil border. The name '*Iguazu*' comes from the local Indian language and means 'big water'. The falls themselves actually consist of over 270 separate falls that stretch for more than one and a half miles. Most of the individual waterfalls are about 200 feet in height. The most famous of them all is known as The Devil's Throat. It is a U-shaped waterfall that is almost 500 feet across and over 2,000 feet in length. UNESCO designated the falls as a World Heritage Site in 1986. The falls are a popular tourist destination in South America.

15 Amazon Rainforest

The Amazon Rainforest, also known as the Amazon Jungle, is located in South America and covers the Amazon River basin. This rainforest is the largest rainforest in the world. The Amazon Rainforest contains several insects, plants, birds, and other forms of life. A wide variety of trees can be found, including many species of myrtle, laurel, palm, and acacia, as well as rosewood, Brazil nut, and rubber tree. Its wildlife includes jaguar, manatee, tapir, red deer, capybara and many other types of rodents, and several types of monkeys.

16 Leaning Tower of Pisa

The Leaning Tower of Pisa is in Pisa, Italy. Its Italian name is *Torre Pendente di Pisa*. The tower is famous for the shifting of its sandy foundations that had led to a significant lean of 5.5 degrees. The construction of the tower began in 1173. Bonnano Pisano was its engineer. In 1990, the tower was closed and the bells silenced as engineers undertook a major straightening project. The tower is 8 stories high. The shape of the tower is cylindrical and to reach the top of the tower, you need to climb the 294 steps spiralling from the inner side of the tower walls. The height of the tower is 58.36 metres from the foundation and 55 metres from the ground.

17 Stonehenge

Stonehenge was built between 3100 and 1550 bc about 8 miles (13 km) north of Salisbury, England. It is a circular group of huge, erect stones. Stonehenge is probably the most important prehistoric monument in the whole of Britain and has attracted visitors from very early times.

There were three main periods of building: the first period beginning around 3100 bc included the digging of a circular ditch and a ring of 56 pits, known as Aubrey Holes.

In the second period, around 2100 bc, huge pillars of rock were brought from southwestern Wales and erected in two concentric circles around the centre of the site. The double circle was never completed and was dismantled during the following period. The monument was remodelled in the third period. A circle of 30 upright stones weighing up to 50 tons each was erected and capped by a ring of stone lintels. These enclosed a horseshoe-shaped formation of five pairs of upright stones, each pair capped with a stone lintel. This final phase of building probably ended before 1500 bc.

Scientists believe that early peoples were able to foretell eclipses of the sun and the moon by the positions of these celestial bodies in relation to the stone monument. The site may have served as an observatory where early rituals or religious ceremonies took place on specific days of the year.

18 Hong Kong Harbour

The Hong Kong Harbour is located between the Hong Kong Island and Kowloon Peninsula. It is also known as Victoria Harbour. During the second night of the lunar year, there is a fantastic display of fireworks one can witness. Hence, it is popular with tourists. It is one of the world's busiest natural harbours. Hong Kong's striking coastline around the harbour creates an exciting view. Cruises set sail from piers on either side of Victoria Harbour. Among the best places to view the Harbour is the Victoria Tower on the Victoria Peak, or from the piazza at the Culture Centre. Rides on the Star Ferry to view the harbour are also very popular among tourists.

19 Sistine Chapel

The Sistine Chapel is in the Vatican City. The chapel was commissioned by Pope Sixtus IV in 1475. It was designed to be the pope's chapel and the site of papal elections. The architect was Giovanni dei Dolci. The frescoes on the ceiling, collectively known as the Sistine Ceiling, were commissioned by Pope Julius II in 1508 and were painted by Michelangelo. They depict incidents from the Old Testament. The Sistine Chapel is a rectangular brick building with six arched windows on each of the two main (or side) walls and a barrel-vaulted ceiling.

20 Burj Khalifa

The Burj Khalifa is a skyscraper in Dubai. It rises 2717 feet (828 m) into the sky. It is the tallest building in the world. The skyscraper has 162 floors. An observation on the 124th floor allows a 360° view of the city. Its construction began in 2004. The costs exceeded $20 billion, and nearly 12,000 people worked on it. The Burj Khalifa has the highest mosque (158th floor) and the highest swimming pool (76th floor) in the world. Fireworks and celebrations highlighted the official opening of the building in 2010.

21 Devils Tower National Monument

The Devils Tower National Monument is in Wyoming, U.S. It was the first American national monument and was established in 1906. It is also known as Bears Lodge. President Theodore Roosevelt proclaimed Devils Tower as the first national monument in 1906. The Devils Tower rises 1267 feet above the Belle Fourche River. It features a natural rock tower, the remnant of a volcanic interruption now exposed by erosion. This 1347-acre park is covered with pine forests, woodlands, and grasslands. Wild animals like the deer and prairie dog can be found here.

22 Great Wall of China

The Great Wall of China is one of the largest building construction projects ever completed. It was built over 2,000 years ago by Qin Shihuangdi, the first emperor of China (221-206 bc). In Chinese, the wall is called 'Wan-Li Qang-Qeng' which means 10,000 Li Long Wall (10,000 Li = about 5,000 km). It was made for defence against raids by the nomadic people. The longest wall in the world, it is an amazing feat of ancient defensive architecture.

It is one of the Seven Wonders of the World and was listed as a World Heritage Site by UNESCO in 1987. The wall winds up and down across deserts, grasslands, mountains and plateaus, stretching approximately 8,851.8 kilometres (5,500 miles) from the east to the west of China.

The wall is a simple structure. It is built of dirt, stone, and brick. Its height ranges from 15 to 30 feet (5 to 9 m), with watchtowers rising at regular intervals above it. It is 15 to 25 feet (5 to 8 m) wide. Along the top runs a 13-foot (4 m) wide roadway. Behind the wall there are, at intervals, permanent camps for troops.

During its construction, the Great Wall was called 'the longest cemetery on earth' because so many people died building it. Reportedly, it cost the lives of more than one million people.

With a history of more than 2,000 years, some of the sections are now in ruins or have disappeared. However, it is still one of the most alluring attractions all around the world owing to its architectural grandeur and historical significance.

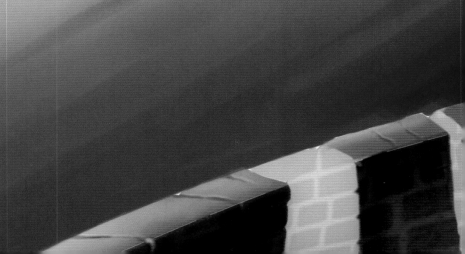

23 Louvre Museum

The Louvre Museum is in Paris. It is called *Musée du Louvre* in French. In 1527, King Francis I razed the original building and started construction on what we know as the Louvre Museum.

Beginning with the reign of Charles V, the Louvre became a place to store works of art. It contained Charles V's private collection of books and artworks. Subsequent monarchs kept adding to the collection.

Today, the grand museum contains more than 300,000 works of art. There are paintings by Leonardo da Vinci, like the *Mona Lisa*, and also works of Raphael. Also on display are famous sculptures, like the *Venus de Milo* and the *Winged Victory of Samothrace*.

24 Buckingham Palace

The Buckingham Palace is in Westminster, England. The palace is the official London residence of the British monarchs. It takes its name from the house built for John Sheffield, Duke of Buckingham. In 1762, George III bought it for his wife, Queen Charlotte, and it became to be known as the queen's house. John Nash converted the house into a palace in the 1820s.

The palace has 775 rooms. These include 19 state rooms, 52 royal and guest bedrooms, 188 staff bedrooms, 92 offices and 78 bathrooms. The palace is 108 metres long across the front, 120 metres deep and 24 metres high. The total floor area of the palace, from basement to the roof covers over 77,000 square metres. The garden covers 40 acres, and includes a helicopter landing area, a lake, and a tennis court. It is home to 30 different species of birds and more than 350 different wild flowers, some of them extremely rare.

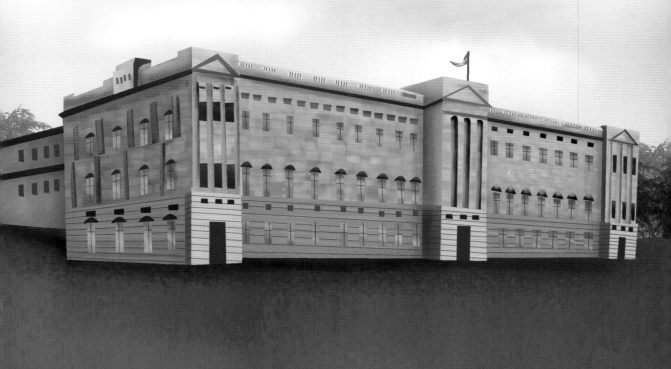

25 Statue of Zeus

The Statue of Zeus is at Olympia, Greece. It was considered one of the Seven Wonders of the Ancient World. This statue was commissioned around 438 bc by the Council of Olympia.

   The statue was built by the Greek sculptor Phidias. It was placed in the huge Temple of Zeus at Olympia. The statue was almost 12 metres (40 ft) high. Zeus was seated on a magnificent throne of cedar wood, inlaid with ivory, gold, ebony and precious stones. In Zeus' right hand was a small statue of Nike, the Goddess of Victory, and in his left hand, a shining sceptre on which an eagle rested. The temple was destroyed in ad 426.

26 La Scala

La Scala is one of the world's greatest opera houses. It is located in Milan, Italy. The opera house opened in 1778. It was designed by Giuseppe Piermarini. The opera house opened with a production of Antonio Salieri's *Europa Riconosciuta*. The building was remodelled in 1867, restored in 1946 after having been bombed in World War II, and renovated in 2002–2004. La Scala has been the scene of many famous opera premieres, among them are Bellini's *Norma*, Verdi's Otello and *Falstaff*, and Puccini's *Madama Butterfly* and *Turandot*.

27 Grand Canyon

Carved out by the Colorado River, the Grand Canyon (nearly 1500 m deep) is the most spectacular gorge in the world and is located in the state of Arizona, U.S. It is 277 mile (446 km) long.

It is noted for its fantastic shapes and colours. The colour of the canyon is red, but each layer has a unique shade—green and pink, buff and gray and brown, slate-gray and violet.

It is home to approximately 70 species of mammals, 250 species of birds, 25 types of reptiles and five species of amphibians. Willow trees and cottonwoods grow there too.

The Grand Canyon, with its mile-high, multicoloured rock walls, craggy cliffs, and sandy slopes, is the embodiment of nature's awesome power and unsurpassable beauty

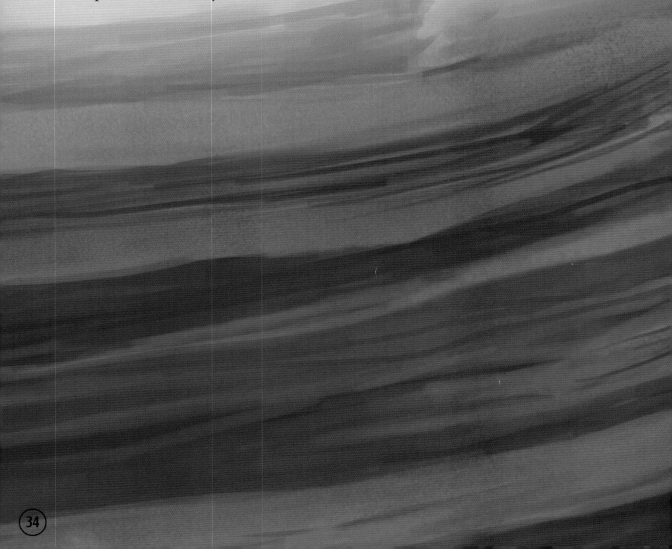

28 Machu Picchu

Machu Picchu was designated a UNESCO World Heritage Site in 1983. It is also one of the new Seven Wonders of the World. It is 7000 feet above the sea level and is nestled on a small hilltop between the Andean Mountain Range. It is the site of ancient Inca ruins. It is believed that the initial residents of Machu Picchu died within 100 years of its establishment due to small pox. It was then captured by the Spaniards and destroyed later. It is often referred to as 'The Lost City of the Incas'.

It was discovered in 1911 by Hiram Bingham, a Yale University professor. Its primary buildings are the Intihuatana, the Temple of the Sun, and the Room of the Three Windows. No one knows what the real purpose of Machu Picchu was. Some people contemplate it was a prison and some say it was a defensive retreat, but the most common belief is that Machu Picchu was the estate of an Inca emperor.

The high level of preservation and the general layout of the ruin are remarkable.

Machu Picchu is the most economically important tourist attraction in Peru, bringing in visitors from around the world.

29 Akashi Kaikyo Bridge

Akashi Kaikyo Bridge, also called 'Pearl Bridge', is located in Japan. The bridge is the longest suspension bridge in the world with a length of 3911 metres (12,831 ft). It is probably Japan's greatest engineering feat. The construction was finished in a span of 12 years. It was completed in the year 1998. The bridge is designed in such a manner that the earthquakes and harsh sea currents do not damage it. It took two million workers to construct the bridge. About 1,81,000 tonnes of steel and 1.4 million cubic metres of concrete were used in its construction. The Akashi Kaiko Bridge acts as a link between the city of Kobe and Iwaya by crossing the Akashi strait.

30 Timbuktu

Timbuktu, also spelled Tombouctou, is a city in Mali. It is historically important as a post on the trans-Saharan caravan route. Timbuktu was a centre for the expansion of Islam (1400–1600). It is home of the prestigious Koranic Sankore University and other madrasas. Timbuktu was founded around ad 1100 as a seasonal camp by Tuareg nomads. The city was designated a UNESCO World Heritage Site in 1988. In the 14th century, Timbuktu became an important focal point of the gold-salt trade.

Its three great mosques, Djingareyber, Sankore and Sidi Yahia, recall Timbuktu's golden age. Although continuously restored, these monuments are today under threat from desertification.

31 Statue of Liberty

The Statue of Liberty Enlightening the World was a gift of friendship from the people of France to the people of the United States on the centenary of American independence in 1886 and is a universal symbol of freedom and democracy. French sculptor Frederic Auguste Bartholdi designed the Statue in collaboration with French engineer Gustave Eiffel.

It is a hollow colossus composed of thinly pounded copper sheets over a steel framework. The statue is 151 feet, 1 inch tall and was the tallest structure in the U.S. at the time it was built.

Visitors climb 354 steps (22 stories) to look out from 25 windows in the crown. They are strongly advised to wear comfortable shoes suitable for climbing small metal steps. The seven rays in the crown represent the Earth's seven seas.

32 Ellora Caves

The caves are an impressive complex of Buddhist, Hindu and Jain temples near the ancient Indian village of Ellora, India. The UNESCO designated Ellora a World Heritage Site in 1983.

There are 34 caves in all: 12 Buddhist caves (200 BC to AD 600), 17 Hindu caves (AD 500 to 900) and 5 Jain caves (AD 800 to 1000). The Hindu caves are the most spectacular in design and the Buddhist caves contain the simplest decoration.

The most extraordinary of the cave temples is Kailasa (cave 16). This temple complex was carved downward and is therefore largely exposed to sunlight unlike the other caves which were carved horizontally into the rock face. It contains elaborately carved structures and halls with stairs, doorways, windows, and numerous sculptures. Other decorations include a representation of the Hindu god Vishnu transformed into a man-lion and battling with a demon.

33 Lord Howe Island

Lord Howe Island is an island dependency of New South Wales, Australia. It is regarded as the most beautiful island in the Pacific and is volcanic in origin. The island was discovered in 1788. It is crescent-shaped with two peaks, Mounts Gower and Lidgbird, each rising above 2500 feet (760 m) at its southern end. Lord Howe Island group had been designated a UNESCO World Heritage Site for its rare collection of plants, birds, marine life and for its incredible beauty and scenery in 1982. The main income of the island is derived from tourism. The area of the island is 7 square miles (17 sq km).

34 Lunenburg

Lunenburg is in Nova Scotia, Canada. This delightful place had its first settlements in 1753. It has retained its original layout and overall appearance, based on a rectangular grid pattern drawn up in the home country. Old town Lunenburg was designated a UNESCO World Heritage Site in 1995. The town of Lunenburg offers visitors many architectural delights. Apart from fishing and fish processing, economic activities focus on shipbuilding and market gardening. The Nova Scotia Fisheries Exhibition and Fishermen's Reunion is held at Lunenburg each September. Historic buildings include St. John's Anglican Church (1754) and Zion Evangelical Lutheran Church (1776).

35 Baishui Terrace

Baishui Terrace is located in Zhongdian, China. The terrace is also known as the White Water Terrace. It is also regarded as the crib of the Naxi culture. The Baishui Terrace was formed by the gathering of calcium carbonate deposits left behind by flowing spring water. The terrace slope is 140 metres long and 160 metres wide and has a semicircular platform pool on the top that is surrounded by white limestone. According to legend, the first saint of the Dongba religion was attracted by the fascinating scenery of this place on his way back from Tibet. Later, the Baishui became known as the holy land of the Dongba religion. Each year, on the eighth day of the second lunar month, the Naxi people gather here to celebrate their traditional festival by singing and dancing.

36 Camargue

The Camargue lies at the mouth of the River Rhone, France. Camargue is Western Europe's largest river delta. It has an area of 300 square miles (780 sq km). Camargue is home to a specialised breed of bull, horses and pink flamingoes. Other animals include sheep, wild boar, beavers, badgers, tree frogs, water snakes, pond turtles. There are some 400 types of birds found here. There are a number of species of insects including one of the most ferocious mosquitoes. It is a place with rich flora and fauna, wonderful parks and museums, and a range of adventure activities. It is also a bird watcher's paradise.

37 Kremlin

The Kremlin came into existence in 1156. It was initially constructed of wood.
In the 14th century, it was rebuilt in white stone. And finally, it was rebuilt in
red brick in the late 15th century by Italian architects. Since then, it has been
repaired and altered on several occasions. Its architecture, thus, reflects its long
history and includes a variety of styles, including Byzantine, Russian Baroque,
and classical. The structure is triangular in shape. The Moscow Kremlin was
designated a UNESCO World Heritage Site in 1990.

38 Pyramids of Giza

The Pyramids of Giza are in Egypt and are the most famous monuments of ancient Egypt. These massive stone structures were built around 4500 years ago. They are the only wonders of the ancient world still standing. The Pyramids of Giza consist of three pyramids: the Great Pyramid of Khufu, the Great Pyramid of Khafre and the Great Pyramid of Menkaure. The Pyramid of Khufu is 230.364 metres square at the base and 137.18 metres high. The Pyramid of Khafre is 215.8 metres square at the base and 136.5 metres high. The Pyramid of Menkaure is 108.5 metres square at the base and 66.5 metres high. The Pyramid of Khufu is also known as the Great Pyramid. The Great Pyramid is truly an astonishing work of engineering skill — for over four thousand years, until the modern era, it was the tallest building in the world. It was constructed using around 2,300,000 limestone blocks, weighing, on an average, 2.5 tons each, although some weighed as much as 16 tons. The ancient ruins of the Memphis area, including the Pyramids of Giza, were collectively designated a World Heritage Site in 1979. The pyramids are amongst the most famous tourist attractions in the modern world.

39 Okavango Delta

The Okavango Delta is in Botswana. It is portrayed as 'the jewel' of the Kalahari. The delta is made up of a network of channels and lagoons. It covers an area of 15,993 square kilometres. It is the largest inland delta in the world.

The delta is home to some of the largest number of wildlife in Africa and is one of Africa's ultimate safari destinations.

There are more than 400 species of birds. Other wildlife includes lions, elephants, hyenas, wild dog, buffalo, hippo and crocodiles, antelopes and other smaller animals like the warthog, mongoose, spotted genets, monkeys, bush babies and tree squirrels.

40 Mount Fuji

Mount Fuji lies on the island of Honshu, Tokyo. Mount Fuji is also known as Fuji-san. It is the highest mountain in Japan rising to 12,388 feet (3776 m). According to legend, an earthquake created Fuji in 286 bc. Mount Fuji is named for the Buddhist fire goddess Fuchi and is sacred to the Shinto Goddess Sengen-Sama, whose shrine is found at the summit. It is the holiest of Japan's 'Three Holy Mountains.' Every summer, thousands of pilgrims and tourists climb to the summit, many of them hiking throughout the night to witness the sunrise from the summit. Its last major eruption was in 1707. Every summer, more than 200,000 people climb to the top of Fuji.

41 Ponte Vecchio

Ponte Vecchio is also known as the Old Bridge as it is one the oldest bridges of Florence. The bridge is characterised by the small houses that line both sides of the bridge. The bridge is built across the Arno River in Florence, Italy. Its builder was Taddeo Gaddi. The bridge was completed in 1345. Originally, the sides held food shops, but by the end of the 15th century, the shops were assigned to goldsmiths and silversmiths. The upper side of the bridge, known as the Vasariano corridor, was designed by Giorgio Vasari to link Palazzo Vecchio and the Uffizi Gallery to the Pitti Palace. It is one of the most famous attractions of Florence.

42 Kunsthistorisches Museum

The Kunsthistorisches Museum is in Vienna. The museum first opened in 1891. It was commissioned by the then emperor of Austria-Hungary, Franz Joseph I. It houses some of the world's most famous paintings and art exhibits. The purpose of this new museum in Austria was to house the art collection of the Habsburgs. Some famous works to be found in the museum include Michelangelo's *Madonna of the Rosary*, *The Crowning with Thorns* and *David with the Head of Goliath;* Raphael's *Madonna in Green;* and works by Rubens, Rembrandt and Titian. It also houses Egyptian, Roman and Greek Art. The museum also has special exhibits from time to time from other museums around the world.

43 Purnululu National Park

Purnululu National Park is in Western Australia. It contains the Bungle Bungle Range. This range is one of the most enthralling physical landmarks of Australia. These are orange and black stripes across the beehive-like mounds, covered in silica and algae. The beehive domes and rocks of the Bungle Bungle change colour from brown to red and orange and gold as the sun travels across the sky. These strange hillocks were the result of erosion over a period of 20 million years. The park is home to other natural phenomena including the Echidna Chasm, Cathedral Gorge and the soaring Piccaninny Gorge. Purnululu National Park was added to the World Heritage list in 2003 for these unique natural towers of sandstone.

44 Walt Disney World

Walt Disney World is in Orlando, Florida. It is a recreational resort owned by the Walt Disney Company. The resort opened in 1971, with just the Magic Kingdom theme park. The resort is spread over an area of 30,500 acres, which makes it approximately the same size as San Francisco. There are four theme parks, two water parks, two night-time entertainment areas, over 20 hotels, six golf courses and much more. Miles of outdoor recreation are available including hiking, biking, boating and swimming. It has three separate areas containing shopping, dining and entertainment facilities as well as a fourth area with nightclubs. A fairly new addition to the resort is the state of the art sports complex where Disney hosts a wide variety of sporting events. Approximately 48 million visitors make the trip to Orlando each year.

45 Grand Place

Grand Place is in Brussels, Belgium. It is one of the most beautiful town squares in Europe. It dates back to the 11th century. There is a spectacular city hall, a Bread House, the King's House and a number of beautifully sculpted stone houses. This is the place where executions took place during the 15th century. UNESCO designated it as a World Heritage Site. Concerts and musical events are organised throughout the year on the square. The Flower Carpet is an event held every two years in August at the Grand Place. It involves the display of millions of fresh colourful begonias. The blooms are kept fresh for four days with the addition of fountains within the pattern on the carpet.

46 Mont Saint-Michel

Mont Saint-Michel is in Normandy, France. It is a rocky islet. It is one of the popular tourist attractions in France. Mont Saint-Michel is almost circular, about 3000 feet in circumference. One of the most prominent features of this island is the tides in its bays which change pretty frequently. Most of the time, it is surrounded by vast sandbanks and becomes an island only when the tides are very high. The island was originally called Mont-Tombe but became known as Mont Saint-Michel in the 8th century. In the Hundred Years' War, the English tried to destroy Mont Saint-Michel but couldn't because it was fortified. The mount is best known for the medieval Benedictine Abbey and church. Mont Saint-Michel was designated a UNESCO World Heritage Site in 1979.

47 Chichén Itzá

Chichén Itzá is in Mexico. Chi means 'mouths', chén means 'wells' and Itzá the 'Itzá tribe'. It was an important Maya city until ad 10th century. After that the Maya civilisation declined and Toltec warriors seized and controlled Chichén Itzá. The remains at the site are neither Mayan nor Toltec but a mixture of both cultures. Chichén Itzá was thought to have been built for the god Kukulcan. El Castillo, a pyramid temple, was dedicated to him. The days and months of the year are represented on El Castillo by the number of steps and terraces. The early buildings are in an architectural style known as Puuc. These earliest structures include the Akabtzib (House of the Dark Writing), the Chichanchob (Red House), the Iglesia (Church), the Casa de las Monjas (Nunnery) and the observatory El Caracol (The Snail). Chichén Itzá was designated a UNESCO World Heritage Site in 1988. It is one of Mexico's most-visited tourist destinations.

There was a well of sacrifice in Chichén Itzá. During drought, victims were thrown alive in the well to provoke the rain god into action. Many victims drowned but those who survived were treated with respect as they were believed to have communicated with the gods.

48 Trevi Fountain

The Trevi Fountain is in Rome. The fountain (Fontana di Trevi) is Rome's largest and most famous fountain. It stands 25.9 metres (85 ft) high and 19.8 metres (65 ft) wide. It was designed by Nicola Salvi in 1732 and competed in 1762. It is famous for its beautiful design and architecture. It depicts Neptune's chariot being led by Tritons with sea horses – one wild, one docile – representing the moods of the sea. The famous custom is to throw a coin into the fountain, thus ensuring your return to the Eternal City. You should toss it over your shoulder with your back towards the fountain.

49 Westminster Abbey

The Westminster Abbey is in London. It is one of England's most important Gothic structures. Almost every English king and queen has been crowned in Westminster, and it is the burial place of 18 monarchs. England's most distinguished statesmen and famous subjects have been given burial in the Abbey since the 14th century. Some of them were Sir Isaac Newton, David Livingstone, and Ernest Rutherford. Part of the south transept is well known as Poets' Corner and includes the tombs of Geoffrey Chaucer, Ben Jonson, John Dryden, Robert Browning, and many others. In 1987, Westminster Abbey was designated a UNESCO World Heritage Site.

50 Anuradhapura

Anuradhapura is one of the ancient capitals of Sri Lanka. This sacred city was established around a cutting from the Buddha's fig tree, brought in the 3rd century bc. It is famous for its well-preserved ruins of ancient Lankan civilisation. From the 4th century bc, it was the capital of Sri Lanka until the beginning of the ad 11th century. During this period, it remained one of the most stable and durable centres of political power and urban life in South Asia. The ancient city, considered sacred to the Buddhist world, is today surrounded by monasteries covering an area of over 16 square miles (40 sq km). The city is designated a UNESCO World Heritage Site.

51 Temple of Emerald Buddha

The Temple of Emerald Buddha is located in Bangkok. It is also known as Wat Phra Kaew. It is the most valued place of pilgrimage in Thailand. The Emerald Buddha statue is about 2 feet tall and is made of green jasper and covered with gold. A visit to Bangkok is not complete without a visit to this temple. The Emerald Buddha is covered in a seasonal costume, which is changed three times a year to correspond to the summer (crown and jewelry), winter (golden shawl), and rainy months (gilt robe and headdress). The clothings which are not in use are kept on display in the Pavilion of Regalia, Royal Decorations and Thai Coins on the grounds of the Grand Palace. No one is allowed near the statue except the Thai king, who conducts rituals at the temple throughout the year.

52 Temple of Artemis

The Temple of Artemis is in Ephesus, Turkey. It is one of the Seven Wonders of the Ancient World. The temple was dedicated to Artemis, the twin sister of Apollo. It was built by King Croesus of Lydia in about 550 BC. The size of the temple was over 350 feet by 180 feet. The temple was destroyed by the invading Goths in AD 262 and was never rebuilt. The Temple of Artemis was the first building made entirely of marble except for its tiled wooden roof. The temple was used as a marketplace and a religious institution. It was visited by merchants, tourists, artisans, and kings who paid homage to the goddess by sharing their profits with her. Recent archeological excavations revealed gifts from pilgrims including statuettes of Artemis made of gold and ivory, earrings, bracelets and necklaces. The temple features many works of art like the four bronze statues of Amazon women.

53 Canterbury Cathedral

The Canterbury Cathedral is in Canterbury, Kent. It is one of the oldest Christian churches in England. It was originally founded in AD 602 by St. Augustine. The cathedral has been designated a UNESCO World Heritage Site. It is the historic seat of the Archbishop of Canterbury. The Christ Church Gateway forms the main entrance into the Cathedral area. The figure of welcoming Christ at the centre is a present substitute of a statue destroyed during the Puritan Revolution. The central Bell Harry Tower is built of bricks and covered with stone. The elaborate carvings are characteristic of the late English Gothic style. There is a magnificent collection of medieval stained glass windows.

54 Bay of Fundy

Bay of Fundy is located on the Atlantic coast of North America, on the northeast end of the Gulf of Maine between the provinces of New Brunswick and Nova Scotia in Canada. The Bay of Fundy is 290 kilometres in length. The mouth of the bay is 100 kilometres wide and between 120 and 215 metres deep. It is a deep, funnel-shaped bay that splits at its northeastern head into the Chignecto Bay and the Minas Basin. The name 'Fundy' is thought to date back to the 16th century, when the Portuguese referred to the bay as 'Rio Fundo' or 'deep river'. The bay contains a diverse ecosystem featuring approximately eight species of whales, an abundance of dolphins, porpoises, fish, seals, and seabirds. The bay is surrounded by breathtaking cliffs, mud flats, and plateaus. Tides approaching a height of 17 metres, the highest in the world, occur in its eastern extremity.

55 Hoover Dam

Hoover Dam is built on the Colorado River at the Arizona-Nevada border. It was once known as Boulder Dam. It was renamed in 1947 to honour President Herbert Hoover. Hoover Dam is the highest concrete dam in the western hemisphere, standing at more than 725 feet above the Colorado River. Its construction was completed in less than five years and well under budget in 1936. It has the world's largest hydroelectric power generating system with 17 generators producing 4 billion kilowatts of electricity every year, and it is still the largest hydroelectric power generator in the United States. It was also voted one of the top ten construction achievements of the 20th century. Besides being a major source of electrical power in the Southwest, Hoover Dam provides irrigation water to the neighbouring agricultural areas and helps in controlling floods in the area.

56 Amalfi Coast

Amalfi Coast is in Italy. The Amalfi Coastline is the most gorgeous and stunning coastline in the world. The coastline begins at Sorrento and ends at Salerno. The Amalfi Coast drive offers a splendid view of the small towns, isolated bays, and deep gorges. It seems as though the towns and villages are clinging to the cliffs which rise from the shimmering blue sea. The Amalfi Coast was designated a UNESCO World Heritage Site in 1997.

57 Drakensberg

The Drakensberg mountain range is in South Africa. The range rises to more than 11,400 feet (3475 m). The local Zulu name for Drakensberg is Quathlamba which means 'the Barrier of Spears'. There are many game reserves and parks within the range. Rock paintings of the Bushmen can be seen in many parts of the Drakensberg. It is the main watershed of South Africa and is the source of the Orange River. The Drakensberg Park was designated a UNESCO World Heritage Site in 2000.

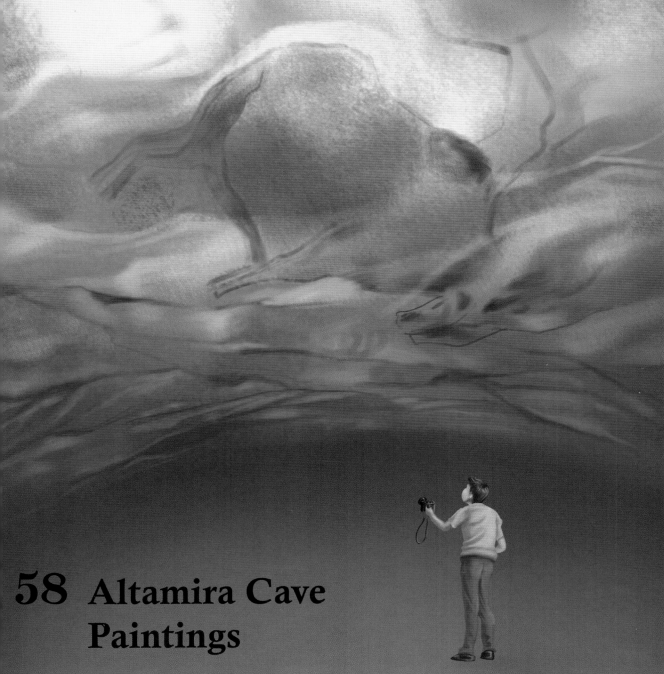

58 Altamira Cave Paintings

The Altamira Cave Paintings are found in Spain. The Altamira site is one of the greatest collections of cave paintings ever discovered. The cave is 296 metres long and consists of a series of twisting passages and chambers shaped like the alphabet 'S'. The paintings depict the beginning of the Magdalenian period, about 15,000 years ago. Altamira was designated a UNESCO World Heritage Site in 1985. The cave was discovered by a hunter in 1868 and was visited in 1876 by Marcelino Sanz de Sautuola, a local nobleman. The paintings of bison, red deer, boar and horses date from 14,000 years ago, and were saved from the ruins of time and corrosion by an earlier landslide, which left them protected.

59 Palenque

Palenque is a ruined ancient Mayan city of southern Mexico. The most important structures at the site are El Palacio (the Palace), which has a tower that rises above the complex; Los Templos del Sol, de la Cruz, and de la Cruz Foliada (The Temples of the Sun, the Cross, and the Foliated Cross). The city's ruins were designated a UNESCO World Heritage Site in 1987. The Temple of Inscriptions is famous for its hieroglyphic tablets and is one of the best-preserved Mayan temples. In 1952, a tomb was uncovered under the Temple of the Inscriptions, representing for the first time that the Maya pyramids served both as funerary structures and temple platforms.

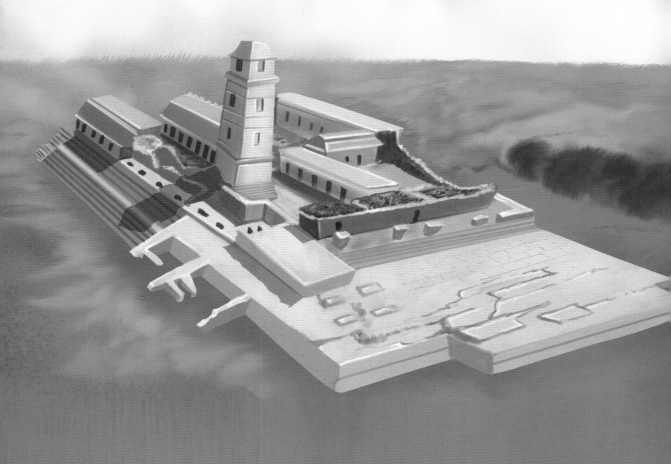

60 Milford Sound

Milford Sound is situated on the south-west of theSouth Island of New Zealand. It is named after Milford Haven. The fjord runs 15 kilometres inland from the Tasman Sea. It is considered to be New Zealand's most famous attraction. More than 5,50,000 people visit the fjord every year. The fjord is surrounded by towering rocks and mountains. Rainforests cover the cliffs, and animals like seals, dolphins, and penguins can be viewed. The sound is the northernmost fjord in Fiordland National Park. It is also the site of a town, Milford Sound, one of the region's few permanently inhabited places.

61 Tubbataha Reef Marine Park

The Tubbataha Reef Marine Park is spread over an area of 33,200 hectares in the middle of the Sulu Sea. It consists of the North and South Reefs and the adjacent Jessie Beazley Reef. The North islet of the park serves as a nesting ground for birds and marine turtles. The park is home to an amazing variety of marine life and features some of the most beautiful coral reefs in the world. Over one thousand species that can be found, many are already endangered species. Animal species found here include manta rays, lionfish, tortoise, clownfish, and sharks. It was designated a UNESCO World Heritage Site in 1993.

62 Upolu

Upolu is an island of sand in Samoa in the South Pacific Ocean. The island is about 46 miles in length and 16 miles at its widest point with an area of 432 square miles (1119 sq km). The island's soil is fertile. Cacao, rubber, bananas, and coconuts are grown here. Agriculture is the main occupation. Pigs, cattle, and chickens are the most important livestock raised on the island. Besides agriculture, the people of Upolu are also engaged in industrial activities. Faleolo Airport offers both domestic and international air service to the island. The endangered flying fox and several types of tropical birds are found here.

63 Trulli District

Trulli District is in Apulia, Italy. The Trulli are one of the most unusual and unique structures in Italy. They are conical, stone-roofed houses. Fanciful, twisted chimneys decorate the rooftop of the houses. These buildings are built of a typical stone from the region. The walls are more than a metre thick, protecting the residents from heat and cold. Ladders leading to upper stories are present outside the houses. The houses are usually found in small clusters. Often, several Trulli are joined together to form a larger complex. The heart of the Trulli region is Alberobello, where there are more than 1000 Trulli built along the narrow streets. This Trulli-rich area of the town has been declared a national monument of Italy.

64 Kiyomizu-dera

Kiyomizu-dera (Pure Water Temple) is a Buddhist temple in eastern Kyoto, Japan. The temple was designated a UNESCO World Heritage Site in 1994. The main hall of Kiyomizu-dera is dedicated to Kannon, the Buddhist Goddess of compassion. It is famous for its vast *verandah*, supported by 139 wooden pillars (each 49 ft high), which juts out over the hillside and offers beautiful views of the city. The Kiyomizu Temple was founded in ad 780 and rebuilt in 1633. In Japanese, '*kiyoi mizu*' means pure water. Drinking the water of the three streams that fall into a pond in the temple complex is said to confer wisdom, health, and longevity.

65 Meteor Crater

Meteor Crater is in Arizona, U.S. It is also called Barringer Meteorite Crater, Coon Butte, Arizona Meteor Crater, or Canyon Diablo. The crater is a rimmed, bowl-shaped pit produced by a large meteorite. The crater is 4000 feet (1200 m) in diameter and about 600 feet (180 m) deep inside its rim, which rises nearly 200 feet (60 m) above the plain. It was discovered in 1891. It is estimated to be between 5000 and 50,000 years old. It is the best-preserved crater on Earth and a popular tourist attraction.

66 Agrigento

Agrigento is a city situated in Sicily, Italy. The city of Agrigento was established in the 5th century BC by the Greeks. It is well-known for a number of archaeological structures. The plateau site of the city is rich in Greek remains. Some important ruins are the Valley of the Temples, Castle of Poggio Diana, Roman Temple of Olympian Zeus, the Fallen Atlas. Some prominent buildings of the medieval and modern city include the 14th-century cathedral, the 13th-century Churches of Santo Spirito and Santa Maria dei Greci, Baroque churches and palaces, and the rich archaeological museum. Agriculture is the main occupation of Agrigento. The world's best strawberries are available here.

67 Colosseum

The Colosseum is an amphitheatre in Rome. Its construction began between AD 70 and 72 during the rule of Vespasian. Titus dedicated it officially in AD 80 in a ceremony which included 100 days of games. The Colosseum measures 620 feet by 513 feet (190 m by 155 m). It was almost exactly like a football stadium today. It was built of concrete, marble and limestone. It was capable of seating 50,000 spectators. It was originally known as the Flavian amphitheatre. It is the largest amphitheatre to have ever been built in the Roman Empire and was oval shaped. Though the colosseum was broken by natural disasters like earthquake, it is still one of the favourite places of tourists. The Colosseum was a place where a lot of people could sit and watch entertainment. The entertainment was mostly people killing animals, or people killing each other.

There were 80 entrances, two being reserved for the emperor and his staff. The central area, the arena, was covered with a wooden floor and canvas to make it waterproof. Over this was a layer of sand to absorb blood. The arena was surrounded by a 5-metre-high

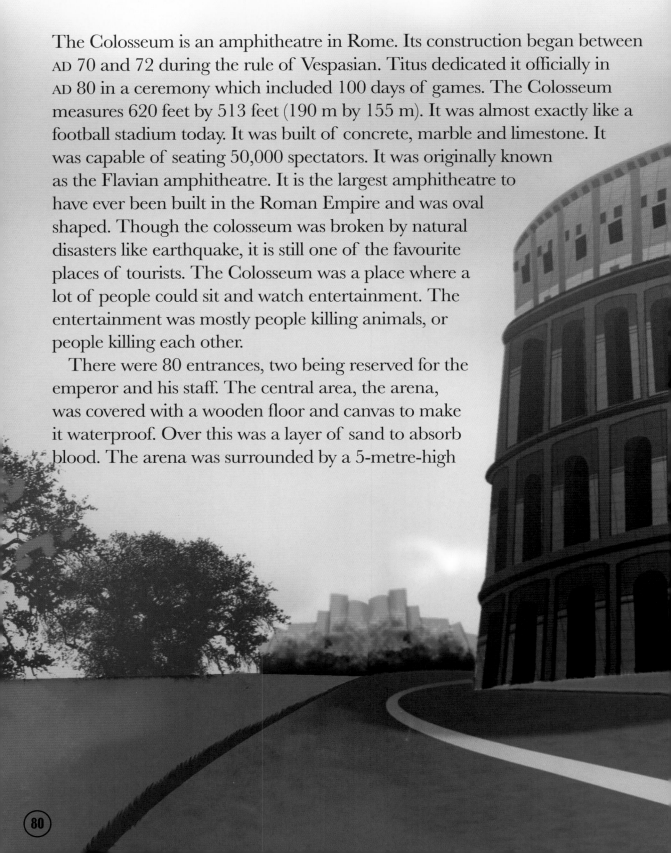

wall to protect spectators from attacks by wild beasts. At the top of the wall was the podium, on which the royals and others important people had their seats. Above this was the cavea or seating area. This was divided into three parts: the lowest for the knights, the middle for wealthy citizens and the top for the general population.

68 Niagara Falls

Niagara Falls is said to be the biggest waterfall on the River Niagara. The waterfall is located between two cities: Niagara Falls, Ontario and Niagara Falls, New York. The Niagara Falls is 27 kilometres (17 miles) long from the north to the northwest of Buffalo, New York and 120 kilometres (75 miles) long from south to southeast of Ontario. It is known both for its splendour and also as the source of hydraulic power. The Niagara Falls is called one of the most romantic places on earth. The Falls at Niagara are about 12,000 years old. There are two parts of this fall: the American Falls and Niagara Falls, Canada usually called Horseshoe Falls. Between them is Goat Island, a tree-covered islet in the middle of the river. The Horseshoe Falls is on the Canadian side of the border. They are supposed to be the best and the most beautiful falls. The name of the falls has been derived due to the shape of the falls. The American Falls is a little less impressive than the Horseshoe as it has almost nine times less water in it and that is why it is not very striking to see.

69 Calakmul

Calakmul is a significant Maya site in Mexico. It is also called the 'City of the Two Adjacent Pyramids'. A snake head emblem has been found on all the artefacts of this region. At its height, during the Classic Mayan Period, the city is thought to have been home to 50,000 people. Of the 6750 ancient structures found at the site, the largest is the great pyramid. It is 55 metres high. It is the tallest of the Maya pyramids. Other noteworthy structures on the site include 117 stelae, many of which come in pairs, as monuments to Mayan rulers and their wives. The city is also known for its murals which, unlike many other known examples, show scenes from all levels of society. It was designated a UNESCO World Heritage Site in 2002.

70 Sun Temple

The Sun Temple of Konark is in Orissa, India. It was constructed in the 13th century by King Narasingh Deva. The entire temple was designed in the shape of a huge chariot with seven horses and twenty-four wheels carrying the Sun God, Surya, across the heavens. The temple also symbolises the passage of time, which is under the Sun God's control. The seven horses, which pull the Sun Temple eastwards towards dawn, represent the days of the week. The 12 pairs of wheels represent the 12 months of the year and the eight spokes in each wheel represent the eight ideal stages of a woman's day. It was designated a World Heritage Site in 1984.

71 Nymphenburg Palace

The Nymphenburg Palace or Nymph's Castle is a baroque palace in Munich, Bavaria, Germany. The palace was the main summer residence of the rulers of Bavaria. The Baroque structure was begun in 1664 by the Prince Elector Maximilian II Emanuel. The circular Hall of Mirrors with silver ornament on a blue background and the symbolic hunting scenes is quite unique. The Nymphenburg gardens have been converted into a public park. The Botanical Garden in the Nymphenburg Park is one of the most beautiful gardens in Germany.

72 Fontainebleau

Fontainebleau is in Paris, France. Its château is one of the largest residences built by the kings of France. The Gallery of Francis I, the horseshoe exterior staircase, the ballroom and the council chamber are some of the things to see. The château is surrounded by pleasant gardens crossed by a canal built in the reign of Henry IV. It is protected by Frances Office National des Forêts, and it is recognised as a French national park. The château at Fontainebleau has architectural elements from the 16th to the 19th century. The national forest of Fontainebleau is one of the most picturesque in France.

73 Zwinger

The Zwinger (*Der Dresdner Zwinger*) is a palace in Dresden, Germany. It is a major landmark of German baroque architecture. The construction of the palace began in 1709 and was completed in 1719. Its construction was ordered by Augustus II, king of Poland, as a place for entertainments, tournaments and royal festivities. Its architect was Matthäus Daniel Pöppelmann. The name 'Zwinger' is taken from the German word '*Zwinger*' meaning the outer ward of a concentric castle. The Zwinger includes six pavilions connected by large galleries. The most impressive pavilions are the Rampart Pavilion (wall) and the Glockenspiel (carillon) Pavilion. The best-known feature of the Zwinger is the Kronentor or Crown Gate—a baroque gate topped by a large crown.

74 Summer Palace

The Summer Palace is in Beijing, China. Its Chinese name, Yiheyan, translates as Garden for Maintaining Health and Harmony. It is one of the largest imperial gardens in the world. There are various things to see here. Some of them are the Marble Boat and the Long Corridor. The Marble Boat is not made of marble but of stone painted to look like marble. The ceilings and the columns of the Long Hall are painted with different landscapes and animal scenes. Some other attractions are Seventeen Arch Bridge, Hall of Benevolence and Longevity and a boat ride on the Kunming Lake.

75 Lemaire Channel

Lemaire Channel is one of Antarctica's most popular tourist destinations. It is found between rocky Booth Island and the mountainous western coast of the Antarctic Peninsula. It is 11 kilometres long and 1600 metres wide at its narrowest point. The place is a perfect destination for cruising in Antarctica. Glacial calving is a common occurrence along the banks of the channel. Penguins and seals can be found here. Lemaire Channel has been nicknamed 'Kodak Gap' due to the number of photographs taken by the visitors while passing through it.

76 Kennedy Space Center

The Kennedy Space Center is located in Brevard County on Florida's east coast. The actual spaceport and launch facilities are located at Cape Canaveral. The Kennedy Space Center is one of the ten NASA centers that serves as America's spaceport. Space shuttle launches are visible from miles around and draw thousands of visitors. The Kennedy Space Center Visitor Complex offers tours of the launch area, views of the giant rockets and even lunch with an astronaut. The Kennedy Space Center is 55 kilometres long, 10 kilometres wide and covers an area of 570 square kilometres.

77 Golden Temple

The Golden Temple is located in the city of Amritsar, India. It was established by Guru Ram Das Ji, the fourth guru of the Sikhs. It is informally referred to as Harmandir Sahib. It is considered the holiest shrine by the Sikhs. It is a symbol of both beauty and peace. The temple is surrounded by a small man-made lake. The temple was built with four doors to show that every religion or faith is allowed to go in to meditate or just listen to the prayers for peace. The entire top of the Golden Temple is made of pure gold and thus adds a lot of pride and beauty to the entire temple.

78 Zion National Park

Zion National Park is in Utah. It is Utah's oldest national park covering about 229 square miles. It is known for its incredible canyons which attract nearly three million visitors each year. The main sections of the park are the Zion Canyon, Kolob Canyon, Kolob Terrace and Highway 9. Wildlife such as mule deer, golden eagles, and mountain lions, also inhabit the park. Zion offers probably the best, most varied hiking of all national parks, including the famous Narrows Trail along the upper stretches of the Virgin River. Zion has a variety of plants—more than 900 species—not found anywhere else in Utah.

79 Christ, the Redeemer

Christ, the Redeemer is a statue of Jesus Christ in Rio de Janeiro, Brazil. The statue is 120 feet tall and weighs 635 tones. It is made of concrete and soapstone. The statue is located at the summit of Corcovado Mountain in Tijuca Forest National Park standing and looking over the city. As a vantage point, it offers superb views of Rio de Janeiro, the bay, Sugarloaf Mountain and Copacabana and Ipanema Beaches. It is a symbol of Christianity and is an important icon of Brazil. There is a chapel for 150 people at the base of the statue. It was designed by Heitor da Silva Costa and created by sculptor Paul Landowski. The statue took five years to construct. The construction was completed in 1931. It has become a symbol of the city and of the warmth of the Brazilian people, who receive visitors with open arms. It is now a part of the new Seven Wonders of the World.

80 Petronas Twin Towers

The Petronas Twin Towers is in Kuala Lumpur, Malaysia. They held the record for being the world's tallest buildings for 6 years before being surpassed by Taipei 101 in 2004. Although they have lost the title of being the world's tallest buildings, Petronas are still the tallest twin buildings in the world. The towers were built by an Argentine-American architect, Cesar Pelli. The construction of the twin towers took 7 years and was completed in 1998. The towers house big shopping malls on their bottom floors. Each tower has 88 floors in it. The towers were designed to symbolise power and elegance using geometric principles typified in Islamic architecture.

81 Kings Canyon National Park

Kings Canyon National Park is in southern Sierra Nevada, California. It was established in 1940. The park has an area of 722 square miles (1870 sq km). It contains groves of giant sequoias including Grant and Cedar groves. The park's most amazing feature is Kings Canyon. The canyons of the Kings River are actually the deepest canyons in North America, deeper even than the Grand Canyon. The park's forests also have sugar and yellow pine, white fir and incense cedar. Animals like deer, black bears, bighorn sheep, etc. are found here.

82 Khajuraho

Khajuraho is in Madhya Pradesh, India. Khajuraho was one of the capitals of the Chandela kings, who ruled from the 9th to the 11th century. It originally had about 85 temples built by multiple rulers from about 950 to 1050. These temples are built in the North Indian Nagara style. The temples have an abundance of sculptures. Most of the temples are built of sandstone, with varying shades of buff, pink, and pale yellow. Of the 85 original temples about 20 are still well preserved. The temples are divided into three complexes. The western is the largest and contains the splendid Shaivite temple, Kandariya Mahadev, 31 metres high. Khajuraho's name derives from the prevalence of 'khajur' or date palms in the area. Khajuraho was designated a UNESCO World Heritage Site in 1986.

83 Natural Tunnel State Park

The Natural Tunnel State Park is in Virginia. The park opened in 1971. The Natural Tunnel is the main attraction of the park. It is a massive naturally formed cave so large that it is used as a railroad tunnel. The creation of the tunnel began more than a million years ago. The walls of the tunnel show evidence of prehistoric life and many fossils can be found in the creek bed and on the tunnel walls. A railroad was constructed through the natural tunnel in 1893. The facilities offered at the park include a campground, picnic areas, amphitheatre, visitors centre with a gift shop, historical blockhouse, swimming pool, and a chair lift to the tunnel floor.

84 Eiffel Tower

The Eiffel Tower is in Paris, France. Built in 1889, it is the tallest building in Paris. It was designed by engineer Gustave Eiffel and named after him. The tower is 300 metres (984 ft) high. It rests on a base that is 5 metres (17 ft) high, and a television antenna atop the tower gives it a total elevation of 322 metres (1056 ft). The Eiffel Tower was the world's tallest man-made structure until the construction of the Chrysler Building in Manhattan. The tower is a hugely popular tourist destination. It is one of the most recognisable structures in the world. The tower has two restaurants and both are located on the first floor.

85 Monte Alban

Monte Alban is located in Mexico. It is situated on a mountain 400 metres above the Oaxaca Valley. It is the place of a ruined site of Zapotec and Mixtec cultures. It was founded approximately around 500 bc and flourished until AD 750. During the Mesoamerican period, much of the state of Oaxaca was controlled from here. Its main structures are the Danzantes (Gallery of Dancers), the Great Plaza, System II, Building J, Central Building G.H., the Palace, the Ball Court, the southern platform, System 7 Deer and Tomb Number 7 of the Great Plaza. The oldest known formation at Monte Alban is the Gallery of the Dancers. The glyphs portray childbirth, dwarfism, captives, the sick, or the dead with twisted body positions (like dancers).

86 Maulbronn Monastery

Maulbronn Monastery is situated on the northern border of Germany. The abbey was built in 1147 by 12 monks. The monastery is surrounded by fortified walls and features an elaborate water management system. It is one of the best preserved medieval monuments in the world. The monastery was built in the Gothic and Romanesque style. Maulbronn was designated a UNESCO World Heritage Site in 1993.

87 Longmen Caves

Longmen Caves are in the Henan province of China. There are some 1350 caves and 40 pagodas with Buddhist statues carved out of the hard limestone cliffs. The carving began in ad 492 and continued for 500 years. Longmen means 'dragon's gate' in Chinese. Ancestor Worshiping Cave is the most famous of all Longmen Caves and is also known as the Fengxian Temple. The caves were designated a UNESCO World Heritage Site in 2000.

88 Sera Monastery

The Sera Monastery is in Lhasa, Tibet. It is at the foot of Tatipu Hill. It is one of the three famous monasteries in Lhasa. The Sera Monastery is dedicated to the Gelugpa or Yellow Hat Sect which is a branch of Tibetan Buddhism, founded by Tsong Khapa. Jamchen Chojey, one of Tsong Khapa's disciples built the monastery in 1419. The word 'Sera' means wild rose in Tibetan language, because the hill behind it was covered with wild roses when the monastery was built. The monastery covers an area of 1,14,946 square metres (28 acres). Its main buildings are the Coqen Hall, Zhacang (college) and Kamcun (dormitory). Scriptures written in gold powder, fine statues, scent cloth and unparalleled murals can be found in these halls.

89 Kashmir

Kashmir is in India. It is a beautiful and popular tourist destination. It is known for its breathtaking scenic beauty. The Dal Lake is a very popular tourist spot in Kashmir. It is surrounded by snow-capped mountain peaks. Kashmir is also known for its romantic Mogul Gardens. Another remarkable feature is the floating vegetable and flower markets. The houseboats or *shikaras* in the Dal Lake are popular with the tourists visiting Kashmir. There are orchards of almonds, apples, apricots, peaches, pears and walnuts. Saffron is also produced here. Buffalo, cattle, sheep, goats, and poultry are among the livestock that are raised. Silk weaving, shawls (especially *pashmina*), woodcarving, brassware and carpet weaving are some of the major industries.

90 Puerto Princesa Subterranean River National Park

The Puerto Princesa Subterranean River National Park is in Philippines. The main feature of the park is a limestone karst mountain landscape with an underground river. The underground river winds through a spectacular cave before emptying into the South China Sea. It is considered to be the world's longest underground river. The river has major formations of stalactites and stalagmites, with several large chambers. The park has a cave that overlooks a clear lagoon bordered with ancient trees around the rim. The beach near the cave is frequented by monkeys, monitor lizards, and squirrels. The park has been designated a UNESCO World Heritage Site in 1972.

91 Le Puy-en-Velay

Le Puy-en-Velay is in France. It is a major pilgrimage town. A red cast-iron statue (53 ft high) of Our Lady of France was erected in 1860 on a hill. At the foot of the hill stands the 11th–12th-century Romanesque Cathedral of Notre-Dame. Le Puy-en-Velay is the starting point of the 1600-kilometre (1000 mile) walking pilgrimage to Santiago de Compostela in Spain. Handmade lace is a popular product here. Industrial activities include food processing and the manufacture of machinery, plastics, rubber, paper and packaging, and textiles.

92 Smithsonian Institution

The Smithsonian Institution is in the United States of America. It is one of the largest museum complexes in the world. It has 18 major museums, a national zoo and a number of research centres. About 20 million visitors visit the institute annually. The complex includes the National Air and Space Museum; National Museum of Natural History; the Smithsonian world-class art museums which includes Cooper-Hewitt National Design Museum, Freer Gallery of Art, Hirshorn Museum and Sculpture Garden, National Museum of American History, National Museum of the American Indian and Natural Portrait Gallery; and National Zoological Park. The institution belongs to and is run by the U.S. Government.

93 Mitla

Mitla is an archaeological site in Oaxaca, Mexico. The Mitla ruins date back to ad 200. The site was built during the Zapotec civilisation. Mitla was a major religious centre. There are five major groups of ruins. At present, only two of them remain. The Columns Group is the best preserved. The House of Pezelao is its major attraction.

94 Petra

Petra is an ancient city in Jordan. It is one of the New Seven Wonders of the World. The site consists of tombs, temples and other monumental buildings carved into solid sandstone cliffs. The Nabataeans sculpted the cliff buildings of Petra. The Nabataeans were an Arab tribe that flourished from around the 4th century bc to ad 106. They were extraordinary engineers who constructed a refined pipe-and-tunnel water system to bring in drinking water and keep out flash floods. Some of the major attractions of Petra are the Byzantine Church, Great Temple, Monastery, the Siq and the Treasury. The Byzantine Church dates back to the 5th and 6th centuries and contains some remarkable Byzantine mosaics. The Great Temple is one of the largest structures of Petra and dates back to the 1st century bc. The Siq is a sandstone canyon consisting of Nabatean carvings and monuments. The Treasury is a favourite among the tourists. Petra was designated a UNESCO World Heritage Site in 1985.

95 Alaska Cruise

On an Alaska Cruise, one passes the fjords lined with glaciers and snow-capped sharp peaks. The two most popular cruises are the Inland Passage cruise and the Gulf of Alaska cruise. The Inland Passage cruise consists of a 7-day round trip out of Vancouver, B.C. (or Seattle, Washington) to the Inland Passage to see its fjords, glaciers and towns. Some of the highlights of the Inland Passage cruise are Glacier Bay National Park, College Fjord and Skagway. The Gulf of Alaska cruise has the Inland Passage cruise as well as a visit to the glaciers farther north.

96 Rhodes Old Town

Rhodes Old Town is in Greece. The topmost feature of the town is the Palace of the Grandmaster. It was the headquarters of the Knights of St. John. Its walls are 4 kilometres (2.5 miles) long. The walls surround both the palace and the town. Other important places include the Great Hospital and the Street of the Knights. The old town was designated a UNESCO World Heritage Site in 1988.

97 Royal Palace

The Royal Palace is in Madrid, Spain. It is also called *Palacio Real* in Spanish. The palace dates back to the 18th century and features beautiful artwork. The Royal Palace is the official residence of the current king but he does not live there. The palace is however used as a museum. It has 870 windows, 240 balconies, 44 sets of stairs and 110 doors. The palace houses a huge collection of classical Spanish artwork by Goya and Velázquez.

98 Romantic Road

The Romantic Road is in Bavaria, Germany. The road takes us through a variety of walled medieval towns, eye-catching castles, and unspoiled countryside in Bavaria. The road starts from Wurzburg and ends at Fussen. The route is also known for passing by the famous Neuschwanstein Castle. Between Wurzburg and Fussen is a town called Rothenburg.

99 Vatican Museums

The Vatican Museums are located inside the Vatican City. There are paintings, sculptures, and other artworks collected by the popes through the centuries. The museums include several architectural marvels such as the Sistine Chapel, the Chapel of Beato Angelico, the Raphael Rooms, the Loggia and the Borgia Apartment. The north end has the Pio-Clementino Museum, Egyptian Museum, Etruscan Museum and Vatican Picture Gallery. The south end contains the Raphael Rooms, Borgia Apartments and Sistine Chapel.

100 Santa Maria delle Grazie

Santa Maria delle Grazie is a church in Milan, Italy. It is famous because it houses the most well-known painting in the world–*The Last Supper* by Leonardo da Vinci. The painting shows Jesus with his 12 apostles. The painting was begun in 1495 and was painted on a plastered wall in the church. It is 8.8 metres (29 ft) wide by 4.6 metres (15 ft) high. Santa Maria delle Grazie was designated a UNESCO World Heritage Site in 1980.

101 Sydney Opera House

The Sydney Opera House is in Sydney, Australia. It is one of the most famous performing art centres in the world. It was completed in 1973. The opera house was conceived and built by Danish architect Jorn Utzon. It has a unique architectural design. The opera house is more than an opera house. It is a performing arts complex with a 2680-seat concert hall and a 1550-seat venue for opera. There are playhouses and studios inside the Opera House as well. There are many bars and restaurants in the opera house. A wide range of performances are staged, including symphonic music, opera, theatre and ballet. It was designated a UNESCO World Heritage Site in 2007.

OTHER TITLES IN THIS SERIES

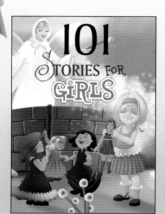

ISBN: 978-93-80070-76-6

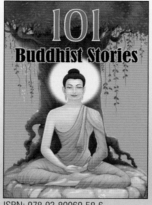

ISBN: 978-93-80069-58-6

ISBN: 978-93-80069-57-9

ISBN: 978-93-80069-59-3

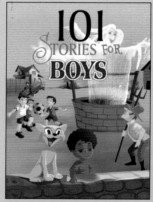

ISBN: 978-93-80070-75-9

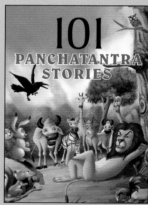

ISBN: 978-93-80070-77-3

ISBN: 978-93-81607-39-8

OTHER TITLES IN THIS SERIES

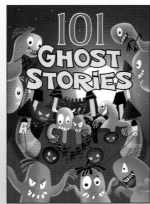
ISBN: 978-93-80069-90-6

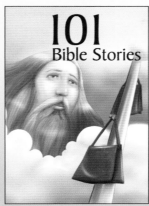
ISBN: 978-93-80069-87-6

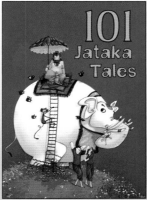
ISBN: 978-93-81607-35-0

ISBN: 978-93-80069-85-2

An imprint of Om Books International